Ankur Khajuria

Academic Foundation Programme (AFP) Secrets

Ankur Khajuria

Academic Foundation Programme (AFP) Secrets

Imprint

Any brand names and product names mentioned in this book are subject to trademark, brand or patent protection and are trademarks or registered trademarks of their respective holders. The use of brand names, product names, common names, trade names, product descriptions etc. even without a particular marking in this work is in no way to be construed to mean that such names may be regarded as unrestricted in respect of trademark and brand protection legislation and could thus be used by anyone.

Cover image: www.ingimage.com

Publisher:
LAP LAMBERT Academic Publishing
is a trademark of
International Book Market Service Ltd., member of OmniScriptum Publishing Group
17 Meldrum Street, Beau Bassin 71504, Mauritius

Printed at: see last page
ISBN: 978-620-2-05440-9

DEDICATION

To my parents, sister and late grandparents for their sacrifice, love and support

CONTENT

Contributors 4

Foreword 6

Preface 7

Chapter 1: UK Integrated clinical academic training and the AFP 9

Chapter 2: Candidate experiences 15

Chapter 3: "I've got a white space" 21

Chapter 4: Clinical emergencies 29

Chapter 5: Critical appraisal for the AFP 39

Chapter 6: Ethics for the AFP 48

Chapter 7: Curriculum Vitae and Portfolios 60

Chapter 8: Practice questions on critical appraisal and clinical scenarios 66

Contributors

Lead author and editor:

Mr Ankur Khajuria, MBBS (Hons) BSc (Hons) FHEA FRSPH MRCS (Eng) Academic Surgery Foundation Trainee, Imperial College London, London, UK

Senior editorial advisors:

Professor Jeremy Levy, MA PhD DSc (Hon) FHEA FRCP, Professor of Practice (Medicine) and Director of Clinical Academic Training, Imperial College London, UK

Professor Afshin Mosahebi, MBBS MBA FRCS (Plast) PhD, Professor of Plastic & Reconstructive Surgery, University College London, UK

Authors:

Mr Mustafa Khanbhai, MBChB (Hons) BSc (Hons) MRCS (Ed), PhD Candidate, Imperial College London, London, UK

Dr Karishma Shah, MBBS BSc (Hons), Academic Foundation Trainee, University of Oxford, Oxford, UK

Dr Hannah Wilson, MBBS BSc (Hons), Academic Foundation Trainee, Imperial College London, London, UK

Dr Nina Cooper, MBBS BSc (Hons), Academic Foundation Trainee, University College London, London, UK

Dr Amit Chawla, MBBS BSc (Hons), Academic Foundation Trainee, University of Warwick, Coventry, UK

Foreword

The integrated clinical academic training pathway in the UK was designed to facilitate and support the brightest trainees wishing to pursue a career in academic medicine. It has been enormously successful. Many of these trainees will go on to lead research groups of their own and advance our understanding of disease processes and their management. Recent published work has highlighted the scarcity of medical students' knowledge and understanding of the Academic Foundation Programme (AFP) application process and this risks students with aptitude not receiving the correct guidance for this process. There is also huge variation around the UK regarding knowledge of these schemes. This book provides up to date experience-based knowledge and skills for medical students to approach the AFP application process with confidence, giving them the maximum chance for a successful application and, we hope, the best start of a productive clinical academic career. The contents may of course be useful beyond the AFP, for example for academic clinical fellowship (ACF) applications. We thoroughly recommend the book and commend the authors on their hard work and the final product.

Professor Jeremy Levy, MA PhD DSc (Hon) FHEA FRCP, Professor of Practice (Medicine) and Director of Clinical Academic Training, Imperial College London, UK

Professor Afshin Mosahebi, MBBS MBA FRCS (Plast) PhD, Professor of Plastic & Reconstructive Surgery, University College London, UK

Preface

The Academic Foundation Programme (AFP) is a unique gateway for junior trainees into the world of academic medicine. The application process for these coveted posts can be a challenging maze and this book has been written to demystify the application process. It has the essential information to understand the skills and attributes being tested. 'AFP Secrets' will provide candidates the armamentarium to tackle the hurdles towards securing a prestigious AFP job. It is important to note that this is not an official resource, but it has been written by top scoring candidates who have amalgamated their experiences, knowledge and skill. It will provide an overview of the UK integrated clinical academic training pathway and high yield guidance on fundamental topics including critical appraisal, research ethics, clinical emergencies and white space questions. Interspersed with this are personal experience accounts from successful candidates and mock interview questions to practice with colleagues.

Mr Ankur Khajuria, MBBS (Hons) BSc (Hons) AICSM FHEA FRSPH MRCS (Eng), Academic Surgery Foundation Trainee, Imperial College London, London, UK

CHAPTER 1

UK Integrated Clinical Academic Training and

the Academic Foundation Programme (AFP)

Mr Ankur Khajuria

Academic medicine is a branch of medicine that is pursued by clinicians who participate in scholarly activities. It has responsibilities in research, teaching and leadership/management. (1) Doctors have a duty to remain up to date and must have the ability to critically appraise evidence to best inform their clinical practice. Despite the importance of academic medicine, recruitment of junior doctors into academia has been of concern globally, with junior doctors often not grasping its importance. Lack of exposure, inflexibility in academic/clinic work balance and lack of a transparent career structure have been voiced. (2) In craft specialties, where undertaking a high number of procedures/operations (such as in surgery) are required to achieve competency, splitting time between clinical and academic responsibilities can be problematic. Academic clinicians may also be judged against the standard of their full-time colleagues, who dedicate majority of their time to clinical work.

The National Institute of Health Research (NIHR) integrated clinical academic pathway (Fig.1) was developed in the UK in 2006 to address these issues. 3 particular concerns to address were (2):

(i) lack of a transparent career structure with a clear route of entry into academia;

(ii) Inflexibility in clinical/academic training balance

(iii) Insufficient structured academic posts on training completion

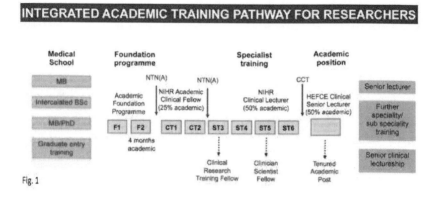

Fig. 1

What is the Academic Foundation Programme (AFP)?

The AFP was designed as the 'first opportunity for research' where newly qualified doctors obtain four months of protected academic time to undertake research, teaching and/or a leadership/management project, as part of a two-year programme. Approximately 450 posts are offered nationally in the UK each year following a competitive selection process with interview. This represents just over 5% of all UK Foundation Programme places. (3) There is great variety of programmes offered, from surgery, medicine to management/leadership programmes. The number of vacancies is similar at the various academic units of application (AUoA). An AUoA is the region offering the programmes that is affiliated with a university. London and South East Thames incorporates all the London foundation schools with one combined application process (124 places in 2017). (3)

The premise of the AFP is not to produce fully-fledged academics. It is an introduction to the world of academia and will be (for most) the first time balancing clinical and academic work side by side. One will also be able to decide whether to take an academic path in the future.

The AFP will help to develop generic skills such as:

- performing a systematic review of the literature
- critical appraisal
- formulating a research question
- developing a robust research methodology to answer the research question
- applying to ethics committees
- writing grant applications
- learning laboratory techniques
- for human studies – learning how to obtain consent, recruit participants
- developing skills in statistics
- developing skills in presenting work nationally/internationally
- developing teaching skills

The table below lists some of the opportunities available to an AFP trainee (the list is not exhaustive):

Skills	Example activities
Research	<ul><li>Projects – RCT, systematic review +/- meta-analysis, cohort studies, cross-sectional studies;</li><li>Basic science/Translational research</li><li>Collaborations (national/international)</li><li>Access to university libraries, journal articles, statistics courses etc.</li><li>Outputs: Presentations, publications, prizes, book chapters, grants</li></ul>
Teaching	<ul><li>Local/regional/national</li><li>Lead a teaching programme</li><li>OSCE/PACES teaching (in turn, revise for MRCS/MRCP exams)</li><li>Teaching qualifications – PGCert</li><li>Anatomy demonstration</li><li>University examiner for summative examinations</li></ul>
Management/ Leadership	<ul><li>Specific 'management' AFP programmes</li><li>Lead a research project (eg RCT) – coordinating recruitment, ethics, funding etc</li><li>Lead a regional/national teaching programme</li><li>Work in collaboration with Business school</li></ul>

Life after AFP

A cross-sectional study conducted on 92 AFP doctors in the UK showed that the choice of work that the trainees carried out during their academic block was independently associated with increasing their wish to subsequently pursue a career in academia. (4) However, it is important to note the AFP is not a pre-requisite to becoming an academic clinician. Non-AFP doctors can potentially achieve more without having had an academic block and have portfolios that match or surpass the quality of their academic counterparts. And one is eligible to apply for an Academic Clinical Fellowship (ACF) or an Academic Clinical Lectureship (ACL) without having done AFP. Having obtained an AFP itself will not differentiate you from other non-AFP doctors. You need to have worked hard and produced outputs. Having protected academic time gives you the opportunity and if used wisely, can greatly build your academic profile.

Academic Clinical Fellowship (ACF)

The AFP can be followed by an academic clinical fellowship with usually 75% clinical time and 25% of time dedicated to research with the ultimate aim of undertaking a research doctorate (PhD or MD). The protected academic time can either be divided into three months per year or one to two days per week or an entire nine months dedicated to research. Towards the end of the ACF programme, one should be able to make a successful application for funding to undertake a MD or a PhD. Entry point can vary. Some are advertised at ST1 level (i.e the three years are equivalent to CT1, CT2 and ST3) and some are advertised at ST3 level. However, to re-iterate, these are not the only routes into a clinical academic career, and many successful academics do not undertake either AFP or ACF posts, and win competitive PhD funding without this support.

13

References:

(1) Khajuria A, Cheng K, Levy J. Effect of a national focused course on academic medicine for UK candidates applying for a Clinical Academic Programme. J R Coll Physicians Edinb. 2017;47(1): 65-69.

(2) Kingston O, Behjati S. (2008). BMJ Careers - Academic medicine. [online] Available at: http://careers.bmj.com/careers/advice/view-article.html?id=2942 [Accessed 17 Aug. 2017].

(3) The Foundation Programme. (2017). The Foundation Programme - Academic. [online] Available at: http://www.foundationprogramme.nhs.uk/pages/fp-afp/faqs/academic [Accessed 17 Aug. 2017].

(4) Lyons OT, Smith C, Winston JS, Geranmayeh F, Behjati S, Kingston O, et al. Impact of UK academic foundation programmes on aspirations to pursue a career in academia. Med Educ. 2010;44: 996-1005

Chapter 2

Candidate Experiences

Mr Ankur Khajuria

Mr Mustafa Khanbhai

It is paramount to speak with seniors who are currently on or have completed the AFP programme that you are hoping to match into. This will provide you with invaluable advice on what specific areas you need to cover to excel in the application process. For example, at Oxford, examiners commonly ask "Can you tell us about a paper you have read recently?" Without this knowledge and not having spoken with someone who has been through the process and consequently not having a substantial response does not look good in an academic interview at one of the most prestigious academic locations.

It is also important to be realistic. If you are ranked low in your year group in terms of your educational performance measure (EPM), it will naturally be challenging to secure a top AFP job. In fact, some UoAs (e.g. London) will not invite candidates for interviews who are below a certain EPM threshold and this may change year on year. Thus, please check directly with the UoA and ensure you fully understand the eligibility criteria before commencing your application. (1) Please carefully read the person specification. Desirable criteria including publications, presentations, prizes will increase your chances of securing an AFP job. However, it is important to note that most candidates will not have publications (and a number of these will secure AFP jobs). Thus, do not let not having a publication deter you from applying if you are academically minded and determined. Below we have included accounts from past successful candidates who have shared their experiences from around the UK.

Dr Karishma Shah, Academic Foundation Trainee, Oxford, UK

"The Oxford AFP is a unique programme that allows trainees to choose their field of interest and their own supervisor. There are 4 white space questions in the application form that focus on past academic achievements, teaching experience, future plans as an academic trainee, and why the candidate wants to go to Oxford.

In the Oxford AFP clinical interview station, you are given a number of short clinical vignettes. You are expected to describe initial management, investigations and escalation plans. The interviewers provide real time feedback of test results and changes in the patient symptoms.

In the academic station, you are often asked about a paper you have read recently. Here, they are evaluating your critical appraisal skills. You are also expected to talk more broadly about your research experiences and how you will build on these at Oxford, and what skills you wish to develop over the AFP period."

Dr Hannah Wilson, Academic Foundation Trainee, London, UK

"Overall my experience was very fulfilling and positive. I relished the chance to 'show off' what I had done outside the restricted remits of medical student life. However, I was unimpressed by the interview in London, which was much more standardised than I had expected i.e. 'what is a p-value?' rather than asking me about what research I had actually done. I have heard reports of more detailed and in depth interviews at other deaneries so I think it is important to be prepared for both. I found reading papers and critiquing them with colleagues the most helpful preparation for the interview. My top advice would be to sell yourself, know your own research and use the minutes wisely. It is a short interview and you have to work hard to condense your thoughts and ideas to really show off your full skill set!"

Mr Ankur Khajuria, Academic Foundation Trainee, London, UK

"Organisation is absolutely key. Print out the timeline of the AFP process and stick on your wall! This kept me motivated. Months before the application form submission deadline, ensure you have finished and submitted any outstanding research papers/audits etc. Peer review takes time, so give yourself maximum time to having a decision on your work before the deadline for AFP submissions. If you haven't already, start putting together a portfolio and CV – this will help you to easily identify previous projects, positions of leadership and teaching to include in your white space questions. Some regions, for example Cambridge, request a CV in place of white space questions. The portfolio will also be a pre-requisite for higher training. Do not underestimate the time required to prepare yourself for the interview. Practise with plenty of mock clinical and critical appraisal scenarios and even record yourself and playback to identify areas to improve. Read about research ethics (see chapter 6) and if/once you secure a job, contact the academic team early to sort out applications for funding and ethics."

Dr Amit Chawla, Academic Foundation Trainee, West Midlands, UK

"The white space questions included regular questions such as, 'what are your reasons for applying to the AFP' and, 'give examples of your research/teaching experience', but otherwise focussed on intangible skills such as teamwork, leadership and adherence to core GMC principles.

The interview was split into two 10-minute stations, occurring in opposite sides of a large room, with multiple applicants interviewed concurrently. One station was academia focussed, with questions such as, 'give three academic achievements, and which are you proudest of?', and, 'tell us about a paper you have read.' There is no abstract to read beforehand as is the case in other deaneries.

17

The other station was mixed, with questions such as, 'how would you prioritise between an academic deadline and clinical commitments?' and 'what skills make you suitable for the AFP?'. Also be prepared for a question about quality improvement, and whether you have any experience with audits."

Please refrain from taking the 'good lines' from a senior's white space answers. It often comes across in one's answers when the style/phrases used are not congruous compared to other text in the answers. Plan ahead and speak to AFP trainees regarding doing mock interviews for you. Mock interviews can also be recorded and watching yourself back may seem daunting but can be incredibly informative. Ultimately, drive and self-motivation are key to not only securing the job but also producing academic output from the AFP.

We finish the chapter with the experience of a trainee who has progressed through the integrated academic pathway and is now undertaking a PhD.

Mr Mustafa Khanbhai, PhD Candidate, Imperial College London, London, UK

"I undertook a BSc degree in Clinical Sciences at The University of Leeds, investigating the effects of Aspirin on fibrin clot structure and function. This was integral in gaining valuable experience in academia early on. It gave me the opportunity to appreciate translational research, refine laboratory skills and overcome hurdles of manuscript writing and publishing. During the final stages of my research, I spent a significant amount of my free time working on the studies, and at no point did I lose interest. If you find research or the process boring or cumbersome, you should re-consider."

"I was accepted on the Academic Foundation Programme (AFP) in North Central Thames, working on databases investigating anaemia in various disease conditions. I was fortunate to experience research that was not primarily lab-based. However, it was a steep learning curve with regards to applying statistics, and I certainly felt out of my depth on occasions. Furthermore, I developed more confidence in networking with other academics during conferences and built professional relationships. I quickly realised that avoiding these situations can result in missed opportunities. The initial awkwardness quickly dissipates as you share ideas and identify potential collaborators, which is essential when applying for grants."

"I secured a NIHR Academic Clinical Fellowship (ACF) in General Surgery, working on medical devices for patients with vascular pathology. This type of research can be volatile as it is patient dependent, and lack of participation or withdrawal can be frustrating. However, seeing a medical device mature in its life cycle and producing evidence that forms national clinical guidance is endearing. Due to the nature of the research, I took a six-month block to focus on my research, however, I completed all the paperwork prior to this, so that I could hit the ground running. Taking time away from clinical work had an impact on my salary, as I was un-banded; however, not having on-call commitments was refreshing."

"Continuing research with a vascular focus, when I wanted to pursue a career in Breast/Oncoplastic Surgery was not ideal. Therefore, I began looking at opportunities that were not speciality specific. This was by far the most challenging period of my academic career. A large number of doctors transition from ACF to PhD within the same research sphere. I reflected heavily on the consequences of my decision. I am now pursuing a PhD at Imperial College London, applying artificial intelligence to patient feedback data, generating insights for quality improvement. I am able to continue with part time clinical work, which is vital when pursuing a craft speciality."

"Time-management and effective communication were important in these academic roles and are skills required to succeed in a symbiotic career as an academic surgeon where one is expected to balance research interests and clinical jobs. Now more than ever, medical students are expected to etch out their career path before they have even graduated. If you are certain you know what you want to do in ten years, you don't. My advice is to be flexible. Like most of you reading this, I too deliberated at length before making any career decisions. But, a significant part of my career has been a series of small serendipities, all of which I am grateful for."

References:

(1) The Foundation Programme. (2017). The Foundation Programme - Academic. [online] Available at: http://www.foundationprogramme.nhs.uk/pages/fp-afp/faqs/academic [Accessed 17 Aug. 2017]

Chapter 3

"I've got a White Space"

Dr Hannah Wilson

Mr Ankur Khajuria

In the words of Taylor Swift, "I've got a blank space baby, so I'll write your name'. Sadly, the white space section of the AFP application is not quite so easy. However, it is definitely not as scary as it first seems. This chapter is dedicated to helping you get the most of the, in the grand scheme of things, very small number of words and white space you have, to sell yourself. This last part is really important. The great British habit of holding back and not appearing to be too outspoken will not work for this section of the AFP. In a very small number of words, you have to list your achievements, provide evidence for them and then state what you learnt from them. It is not easy to do all this whilst answering the question exactly how 'they' want you to.

Now as has already been mentioned in the book, it is important to note that this is not an official resource for how to write the white space. A mark scheme for these has not been officially released and so we write about our own experiences and lessons that we have amalgamated together across the deaneries for general advice of how to tackle these. Each deanery has slightly different requirements and exploring the emphasis and requirements for this part of the application requires careful searching on each individual deanery's website. It is paramount that you have a look at the person specification for the unit of application you are applying to and tailor your responses accordingly. (1)

Think carefully before applying to the AFP but always remember that clinical and academic medicine really do go hand in hand. (2) Thus, preparing for the clinical component of the AFP will provide you a head start for your Final MBBS examination revision.

General Structure

As above, the structure of the white space is variable between deaneries. In general, there are three to four questions each requiring approximately 200 words. Although, certain regions like Cambridge require a CV. The idea is that the white space acts as a focused and condensed version of the CV. Each question has specific parts which all need answering. We will use some examples below to break this question down to find out what the deanery is looking for.

Question 1:

"We recognize that applicants will have had varying levels of research, management and teaching experience. Please give one example from your post-secondary education career to date, of a research project, management or teaching experience and its significance to your application for an academic foundation program".

As highlighted above it is important to follow the question exactly. Points would be lost here for giving two separate examples or not referencing why it is relevant and significant to your AFP application specifically. This requires you to think about what skills you will need for the AFP and/or what qualities would be desirable.

Question 2:

"Please give one detailed example to describe your contribution to academic life during your medical school career and how it will be relevant to an academic medical career"

This question highlights the need to think further ahead. It is asking you to link what you have learnt so far at medical school to the skills you may or may not need in your future academic career. This is harder than it looks but is what will make you stand out. (3,4) This involves thinking about the sorts of things you may be doing in an academic post in the future. Examples include teaching experience and linking to the potential to lecture in the future; research experience and interactions with leaders of the laboratory and the multi-disciplinary team (biomedical scientists, designers, clinicians) suggesting you have thought about the kind of work and skills involved in running a lab/clinical trial in the future (being able to coordinate a team of scientists and clinicians to perform translational research). (5) Whilst a publication reflects the end result of research, this question is more about what you learnt as opposed to what you achieved. (6)

Question 3:

"Academic medicine requires an individual to work successfully in a team. Describe a time that will be relevant to your foundation training when you have worked as a successful member of a team and identify your role and contribution to this success"

Again, this question is looking for specific examples of when you have been involved in a team, either as a leader or a team member and how you personally made it more successful. If you were the leader this might seem more straightforward. Maybe you used good communication or organisation skills to

23

ensure that deadlines and achievements were reached. If you were a team member, maybe you encouraged others, worked well with the leader and/or suggested ideas. The important thing in this kind of question is that you answer exactly what **you** did. So, you must be bold and state your skills and achievements. There is some very helpful advice on applying such techniques in published literature, and you can utilise these to make your own answers more evidence-based. (7,8)

The first important step to mastering the white space is to read and understand the question. As we have done above, highlight the important part of the question and ensure you answer both parts. The main structural tip is that you are relating something you did previously to something you will go on to do in the future. This is to reflect an appreciation for the career you are applying for.

Examples to use in questions

The next part of this chapter is to think about the kind of examples that you could use in answering these white space questions. Some examples to think about include: Research (designed and lead a project); Teaching (medical student mentor/tutor); Team work/Management (president of medical school society); and academic contribution (BSc course representative). These examples are realistic examples of what you may have done throughout your degree. However, what you have done is much less important than what you learnt from said experience. And more specifically what skills you learnt. We have produced the following figure (Figure 1) as a list of qualities that might be reflected or learnt from such experiences.

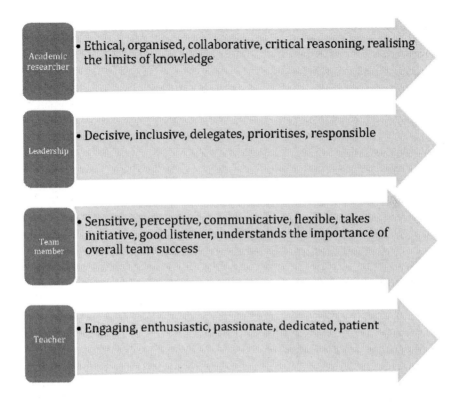

Academic researcher
• Ethical, organised, collaborative, critical reasoning, realising the limits of knowledge

Leadership
• Decisive, inclusive, delegates, prioritises, responsible

Team member
• Sensitive, perceptive, communicative, flexible, takes initiative, good listener, understands the importance of overall team success

Teacher
• Engaging, enthusiastic, passionate, dedicated, patient

FIGURE 1

The above table is by no means a definitive list, but it is important to get you thinking about what skills relate to what kind of experience.

Example Answers

As above, there is no official mark scheme. But we have amalgamated what we know and think and can provide an effective answer. If asked a question as above in Question 1. It is important to think:

What? *Why?* and significance

"We recognize that applicants will have had varying levels of research, management and teaching experience. Please give one example from your post-secondary education career to date, of a research project, management or teaching experience and its significance to your application for an academic foundation program".

"I introduced an online platform where learning materials and lecture recordings could be shared. *Additionally, I initiated a message board where students and lecturers cooperated to resolve each other's queries.* This approach is observed in translational medicine, where patient outcomes drive multidisciplinary collaboration, which encourages pharmaceutical development or amends clinical policy. In my career, I aspire to be involve in harnessing multicentre expertise and study participation when striving for clinical excellence"

Help and Advice

It is important to highlight that the White Space is **your** chance to show what **you** have done. It should be **your** words. Therefore, it is important not to ask too many people to review your white space answers. This could lead to too many conflicting opinions on your work and the wording becoming less like your own. This may seem unimportant but the white space can, and often will provide the point of reference for interview in certain deaneries, so you should know the questions and answers inside out.

Conclusion

We hope this short chapter provides a useful insight into how to approach the white space section of your AFP application. Although at first it seems daunting, you are applying for an AFP because you are committed to enhancing the future of medicine through both research and teaching. This is your chance to show off what you have done so far and how it applies to your future career and demonstrate how and why you will succeed. Take your time, think hard and show off all your skills...Good luck!

References:

(1) The Foundation Programme. (2017). The Foundation Programme - Academic. [online] Available at: http://www.foundationprogramme.nhs.uk/pages/fp-afp/faqs/academic [Accessed 20 Aug. 2017].

(2) Ologunde R, Di salvo I, Khajuria A. The canmeds scholar: the neglected competency in tomorrow's doctors. Adv Med Educ Pract 2014; 5: 383–4.

(3) Mulla S, Watmough S, Waddelove C. medical students' views and understanding of a career in academic medicine. Br J Hosp Med 2012; 73: 401–5.

(4) Blatt B, Plack M, Suzuki M et al. introducing medical students to careers in medical education: the student track at an annual medical education conference. Acad Med 2013; 88: 1095–8.

(5) Sánchez JP, Sastillo-Page l, Spencer dJ et al. commentary: the building the next generation of academic physicians initiative: engaging medical students and residents. Acad Med 2011; 86: 928–31.

(6) Griffin MF, Hindocha S. Publication practices of medical students at British medical schools: experience, attitudes and barriers to publish. Med Teach. 2011;33(1):e1–e8.

(7) Spencer J. Learning and teaching in the clinical environment. BMJ. 2003 Mar 15; 326(7389): 591–594.

(8) Neher J.O et al. A Five-Step "Microskills" Model Of Clinical Teaching. J Am Board Fam Med July 1, 1992 vol. 5 no. 4 419-424

CHAPTER 4

Clinical emergencies

Mr Ankur Khajuria

In most programmes, the clinical station is weighted much more compared to the academic station. Academic trainees must be clinically sound, safe and possess knowledge and skills that will allow them to acquire all the necessary clinical competencies with less clinical time compared to their non-academic colleagues. Candidates have been known to have strong academic CVs but who have not performed optimally in the clinical stations; consequently they have not managed to secure an AFP job. Thus, it is paramount that candidates spend time acquiring the clinical knowledge (especially of clinical emergencies) and become comfortable in articulating this in a structured and logical manner. This will also be very useful for medical school final examinations. In this chapter, we will go through the common clinical scenarios that a candidate may encounter and how to structure the answers to score top points. This chapter will not go through the specific management of emergencies. This information can be sought from resources mentioned at the end of this chapter, but the focus will be on structuring answers and what to say in the interview station to score marks.

For all scenarios, one may wish to articulate, "patient safety would be my absolute priority". This is a key statement and straight away tells the examiner that as a junior house officer, you would prioritise patient safety above all else. It is also a confidence statement, when you maybe particularly nervous at the start of a station, having a firm reflex statement will allow you to ease into the discussion with the interviewer. Depending on where you interview, you may be given 2 or 3 different patient vignettes and asked to prioritise which patient you would see first. In reality, there is more than one member in the team, ie Senior House Officer (SHO) as well as Registrar. If you as the house officer are asked to see two unwell patients in the scenario, you can say that you would see patient X first (and justify why) and subsequently patient Y. You can additionally say that as a safe clinician, you would inform your senior that there may be two potentially unwell patients and that you are going to see one of them first and that the other patient needs a review by another member of the team.

If the scenario says that you have been called by the nurse, you can gather more information on the phone. You would especially want to know the patient's observations, in particular the trend. For example, a blood pressure of 90/60 maybe less worrying, especially if all previous readings are similar! You can request the nurse on the phone to attach cardiac monitoring, obtain an ECG, site a cannula, have crash trolley nearby! Next, say to the examiner that you would then start thinking about differential diagnoses for the scenario. Listed below are scenarios that are either past AFP scenarios or the ones frequently encountered by the house officer (and thus examinable in the AFP interview).

Please note that this list is not exhaustive:

Dyspnoea
Arrythmias
Acute abdomen
GI bleeding
Sepsis
Hypothermia
Hypoglycaemia
Electrolyte disturbances (Hyper/hypokalemia; hyper/hypocalcemia; hyper/hyponatremia; acute kidney injury)
Trauma

We will come back to some of the scenarios later. Whatever the scenario, you will always start your assessment of the patient with the primary survey (ie ABCDE). (1) Simply mentioning that you would follow "an ABCDE" approach will not score you marks. You must say exactly what you would do. Below, you will find a detailed summary of the primary survey and what I recommend on how to structure your discussion.

TIP 1:

If you are confident, continue to talk through the primary survey unless the examiner interrupts you!

Airway:

"Initially, I would follow advanced life support (ALS) principles and perform a primary survey. The first thing I would assess is whether the airway is patent. I would check if the patient is vocalising in complete sentences – if so, I can assume the airway is patent. I would look, listen and feel. Look inside the mouth for any secretions that can suctioned as well as for rash, angioedema, listen for stridor or gurgling and feel for expired air. If the airway is not patent, I would perform manoeuvres. These will include chin lift or jaw thrust (if any C-spine concerns) and use of adjuncts, such as an oropharyngeal or a nasopharyngeal airway. If the airway is still not patent, I would put out a peri-arrest call."

Stridor:

Upper airway obstruction – FAST bleep the anaesthetics and ENT registrars immediately. IM adrenaline 1:1000

Breathing:

"I would assess the effort, efficacy and effect of breathing. I would look for any evidence of respiratory distress – use of accessory muscles of respiration, nasal

31

flaring. I would check the SpO2, the respiratory rate and administer high flow oxygen via a non-rebreathe mask. I would then: Look, Listen and Feel.

Look for symmetrical chest expansion, listen to ensure equal air entry, wheeze and feel for a central trachea, expansion, percussion.

Adjuncts to my assessment would include an arterial blood gas (ABG) and a portable chest radiograph (CXR).

TIP 2:

"In a trauma setting, I would look out for ATOM FC (Airway obstruction, Tension pneumothorax, Open pneumothorax, Massive haemorrhage, Flail chest and Cardiac tamponade)".

Refer to Advanced Trauma Life Support (2) if you would like further information although you would likely not be expected to manage trauma patients in the interview scenario.

THEN REASSESS - If poor or absent respiratory effort, I would Bag-valve-mask the patient and call the arrest team.

TIP 3:

Beware, at any point, the examiner may ask you a question and interrupt your flow. For example, "if the trachea is not central, what could be the cause and what would be your management?"

TIP 4:

ALWAYS say that you would go back and re-assess – "ensure that the airway is still patent. Once happy, I would move onto C."

Circulation:

"I would check the pulse (rate, rhythm, volume and character). A systolic blood pressure of atleast 80 is required for a peripheral pulse. I would check BP in both arms and calculate the pulse pressure, measure capillary refill and request the nurse to get a 12 lead ECG and cardiac monitor. I would establish IV access via short, wide bore cannula (Pousielle's law) (3) in antecubital fossae bilaterally and send bloods for FBC, U+E, Clotting, X-match, cultures and troponin. If the patient is hypotensive, I would consider 500-1000mls warm crystalloid fluid. I would repeat fluid challenge and if no response, call for senior help. If blood loss, one would need access to blood products and massive haemorrhage protocol may have to be put out. I would then re-assess airway (ensure it is still patent), breathing and then I would move onto D.

TIP 5:

"In a trauma setting, I would look for blood on the floor and four more – chest, abdomen, pelvis, long bones." (2) Refer to Advanced Trauma Life Support if you would like further information although you would likely not be expected to manage trauma patients in the interview scenario.

Disability:

"I would assess the patient using the Glasgow coma scale; if less than 8, I would call the anaesthetist [AVPU scale equivalent (P = GCS 8)]. I would also obtain a capillary blood glucose level. I would check whether the pupils are reactive to both light and accommodation (PERLA). I would check the patient's posture and examine tone in all 4 limbs and check plantar response.

TIP 6:

If suspecting overdose → have antidotes such as flumazenil, naloxone ready.

I would then re-assess ABC, then move onto E.

Exposure:

"I would check the temperature. Look for injuries and rashes, check the calves for any evidence of a deep vein thrombosis. I would check for any indwelling catheters".

"I would then re-assess and alert my senior"

That is your primary survey complete. As I mentioned, you may be interrupted at several points, but if you have practised saying the above over and over again, then you should be able to re-start where you left off after addressing the examiner's question, without being hesitant.

TIP 7:

Practice 'saying' the primary survey over and over again. Record yourself if you have to, but on interview day, you should be slick at presenting it on 'autopilot mode'.

The primary survey will actually form the bulk of your interview. There may be slight variation in terms of level of detail required/type of information required based on your unit of applications (UoAs). Thames (one of the biggest and often oversubscribed UoAs) will very much follow the format above. Other regions, for example, Oxford may have more clinical vignettes and may ask more direct questions – e.g. "The potassium comes back 6.5 on the gas; how would you manage this?" or "what is the cause of this acutely unwell patient's deranged renal function". However, still, initial assessment will be ABCDE!

TIP 8:

Speak to friends/colleagues/trainees working in the region you are applying for. You will obtain useful information.

Structuring your answers will differentiate you from the other candidates. I find that it is easier for you to devise your own way to structure, for example, differentials for symptoms.

Example:

Causes of dyspnoea

Respiratory:

- Upper airway obstruction (anaphylaxis, secretions, foreign body)
- Pulmonary vascular disease (Pulmonary embolism)
- Obstructive airway disease (Asthma, COPD)
- Pleural disease (pneumothorax; pleural effusion)

Cardiac:

- Structual (ACS, MI)
- Arrhythmia (Tachy or Brady)
- Obstructive (pre-valvular, valvular, supra-valvular)

Shock

-Pump failure (Cardiogenic shock)

-Peripheral circulation failure

- Haemorrhage
- Fluid loss (D&V, burns, third space losses eg pancreatitis)
- Distributive shock (Sepsis; anaphylatic shock)

-Metabolic acidosis (DKA)

-Drugs (salicylate overdose)

You do NOT have to use this schema, and I encourage you to develop your own ways of structuring – this will make it more memorable and will come more naturally to you in an interview.

Finally, without going into too much detail, I have listed below the key must-know management for common scenarios that you should know. This will be useful not just for the interview but also for your house officer and senior house officer jobs.

SEPSIS:
- Known the difference: SIRS V Sepsis V Severe Sepsis V Septic shock
- Sepsis care bundle
- 3 IN, 3 OUT within 1 hour
- IN: High flow Oxygen, IV fluids, IV antibiotics
- OUT: blood cultures, (Hb + Lactate) + Urine output

INFECTIVE EXACERBATION OF COPD (IECOPD):
- ABCDE
- Controlled O2 therapy with Venturi mask
- Salbutamol 5mg, Ipratropium 0.5mg neb
- IV hydrocortisone 200mg and/or PO Pred (50mg)
- Antibiotics (200mg Doxycycline)
- NIPPV if pH <7.35 or RR >30

UPPER GI BLEED:
- NBM
- Major haemorrhage protocol?
- Alert surgeons, on call endoscopist....
- IV access – Bloods; what size cannula? (Pouiselle's law)
- Fluids

- Clotting abnormalities
- Rockall/Blatchford scoring

ANAPHYLAXIS:

- ABCDE
- Remove cause, raise feet
- Adrenaline 0.5mg (1:1000)
- Chlorphenamine 10mg; Hydrocortisone 200mg IV
- Alert ITU/CCOT/Anaesthetist early

ACUTE MYOCARDIAL INFARCATION

- ABCDE
- MONA – Morphine (5-10mg; with metoclopramide 10mg); Oxygen, Nitrate (GTN), 300mg Aspirin + 300g Clopidogrel +/- 2.5mg Fondaparinux
- Percutaneous coronary intervention (PCI)
- Some examiners still like to ask about indications and contraindications for thrombolysis.

ACUTE PULMONARY OEDEMA

- ABCDE
- Diamorphine 2.5-5mg IV
- Furosemide 40-80 mg IV
- GTN 2 puffs SL
- Read about swan-ganz catheter, understand BIPAP v CPAP

Past example scenarios (asked to prioritise and justify):

- A patient who had collapsed
- A patient who had a degree of heart failure and was breathless
- An angry relative

To reiterate, the clinical station is heavily weighted more compared to academic station. If you prepare well, this is an easy station to score highly and get a lot closer to your dream AFP job!

Good luck!

References:

(1) Thim T, Krarup NH, Grove EL, Rohde CV, Lofgren B. Initial assessment and treatment with the Airway, Breathing, Circulation, Disability, Exposure (ABCDE) approach. Int J Gen Med. 2012;5117-121.

(2) Kool DR, Blickman JG. Advanced Trauma Life Support. ABCDE from a radiological point of view. Emerg Radiol. 2007;14: 135-141

(3) Brzezinski W. Chapter 16 Blood Pressure. In: Walker H, Hall W, Hurst J. (eds.) Clinical Methods: The History, Physical, and Laboratory Examinations. 3rd edition. 1990. Pages 95-97

Chapter 5

Critical appraisal for the AFP

Dr Karishma Shah

Mr Ankur Khajuria

Introduction

Critical appraisal is an essential skill for clinicians. It is common for patients to present doctors with information they have read in newspapers or on the internet, asking for whether new drugs/treatments can improve their care. As doctors, we have a responsibility to analyse the information provided and then to present this in a clear and concise manner.

Interviews for the Academic Foundation Programme (AFP) often dedicate half the time to an academic interview, ranging from critically appraising an abstract to discussing potential projects for the future. However, being able to do this in a time-pressured environment with your future bosses watching over you is frightening for most! Even for non-academic trainees, their role is never purely clinical. There are always opportunities to become involved in academic work and both the General Medical Council (GMC) (1) and The United Kingdom Foundation Programme Office (UKFPO) (2) expect all trainees to engage in some form of academic work.

Research studies can be ranked using the evidence-based medicine (EBM)-pyramid (Figure 1). Systematic reviews and meta-analyses are placed at the top of the evidence hierarchy, as they compile the evidence from multiple smaller studies. (3) However, during an AFP interview it is more likely that you will be asked to interpret a randomised controlled trial (RCT) or a cohort study as these generate interesting discussion points related to blinding, randomisation, bias and ethics, understanding of which is fundamental for junior clinical academics.

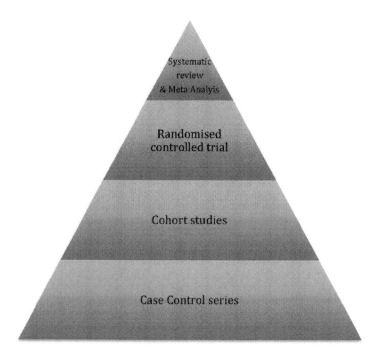

Figure 1: The evidence-based medicine triangle

Critical appraisal is the ability to judge the quality of research and set the results in clinical context. In an AFP interview, and indeed during training, we often need to critically appraise abstracts or papers quickly. All evidence can be analysed succinctly and systematically using a reporting guideline (Table 1).

Study Type	Reporting Guideline
Systematic review & Meta analysis	Preferred Reporting Items for Systematic Reviews and Meta analyses (PRISMA) (4)
Randomised controlled trial	Consolidated Standards of Reporting Trials (CONSORT) (5)
Cohort/case-control study	The Strengthening and Reporting of Observational Studies in Epidemiology (STROBE) (6)
Case reports	Consensus-based Clinical Case Reporting (CARE) (7)

Table 1: Reporting guidelines for different study types

During a short and focused interview, arguably one of the most efficient critically appraisal methods to use is the PICO framework (Table 2). (8) The PICO process focuses on the study itself and is comprehensive. You can build on this to include types of biases and other important factors relevant to interpret the study. It is also important to assess the title of the study, the quality of the publishing journal and the peer-review process.

• P	Population
• I	Intervention
• C	Control
• O	Outcome

Table 2: PICO framework

In this chapter, we will discuss useful steps to efficiently and effectively appraise abstracts during an AFP interview using relevant reporting guidelines and the PICO method. Candidates should use buzzwords such as "bias", "confounding factors", "generalizability", to show they understand the components of the reporting guidelines and are able to use them practically. These buzzwords also make the presentation of a critical appraisal far more structured, highlighting salient points and preventing wastage of both time and words.

This chapter is created to act as a practical guide with examples of how to present your findings. We will focus on a RCT and a cohort study.

3.0 Worked example of appraising a Randomised Controlled Trial

Example

Read the abstract of:

"The late effect of intraoperative wound infiltration with local anaesthetic in surgical patients; is there any? A randomized control trial." By Lanitis et al, 2015. (9)

Below is an example of how to present a critical appraisal of this abstract using points from the CONSORT and PICO methods.

3.1. Example of how to present your critical appraisal in 3-4 minutes

Basic Information:

"This study is a randomised controlled trial analysing the pain effect of infiltrating wounds in general surgery patients with local anaesthetic compared to a placebo. It is well suited to a surgical journal."

Population:

"All patients were recruited from the same speciality (general surgery). Patients were recruited consecutively, reducing the chance of sampling bias. However, there is no information on the type of surgery they underwent or any other inclusion and exclusion criteria. The authors state that there was 'no significant difference … in all known confounding factors". However, we do not know which confounding factors they adjusted for. It would be prudent to know whether the baseline characteristics of the groups were homogenous. This would need to be clarified by reading the whole paper."

Intervention and Control:

"This study compares 15ml of 10% ropivacaine to placebo. However, there is no information on what the placebo actually was (normal saline, water for injection etc), nor how much of it was used. The volume may itself result in pain through a pressure effect. There is also a high risk of performance bias due to the nature of the intervention. There is no information on ethical considerations. "

Outcome:

"The outcome of the study was pain. However, there is no information on the type of pain score used. The abstract does not discuss statistical analysis or p values and levels of significance. Similarly, there is not enough information to calculate a number needed to treat. The entire paper would need to be read to find out more about the statistical methodology used."

Conclusion:

"I do not feel the authors' conclusion can be fully explained by the results presented in the abstract alone. There is no statistical data and the study only compared pain outcome in days 1-7, not in the long-term. Clinically, analysis of how to control post-operative pain would be useful once patients are on the ward, and may be associated with faster recovery times. There is no information on the demographics of the patients included in this study, so the data cannot be generalised to a larger population without obtaining additional information."

4.0 Worked example of critically appraising a cohort study

Example
Read the abstract of:
"Creation of the ideal gastric tube: Comparison of three methods: A prospective cohort study" by Kimura et al, 2016. (10)

Below is an example of how to present a critical appraisal of this abstract using the PICO method.

4.1. Example of how to present your critical appraisal in 3-4 minutes

Basic Information:

"This study is a prospective cohort study analysing three methods of gastric tube creation. It is well suited to a surgical journal. This journal includes both medical and surgical studies, indicating a wider audience."

Population:

"Participants who had gastric tube reconstruction after oesophagectomy, secondary to oesophageal cancer, were recruited between 2012-14. There is a large recruitment time and there is no information on how patients were recruited; this may introduce the risk of selection bias. In addition, there is no comment on the background characteristics of the patients in each group and the number of patients in each group, increasing the risk of confounding factors."

Intervention and Control:

"The abstract does not clearly state what the three different methodologies were. The whole paper would need to be consulted to confirm this. There is also no information on blinding, increasing the risk of both interventional and expectation bias."

Outcome:

"Cost is the primary outcome. However, there is no information on why this was chosen as the primary outcome (for example, what is the relationship between cost and clinical care). The results section also comments on multiple outcomes, such as anastamotic leaks, which are not stated in the methodology section. Similarly, the follow-up period is not defined, increasing the risk of late-look bias." It is not clear whether intention to treat analysis was employed which may contribute to attrition bias.

Conclusion:

"Overall, I feel this abstract does not provide an overview of the paper. It lacks information such as the interventions analysed and it is not clear in the methodology what the outcomes to be measured are. There is not enough information on how bias and confounding factors are controlled for. The entire paper will need to be read to gain a better understanding of the study and its quality. It is therefore difficult to comment on the relevance and generalizability of these results to the wider population."

5.0. Conclusion

There are multiple ways of critically appraising abstracts. Using PICO is just one method, and due to its simplistic structure it allows you to build upon it, for example by commenting on biases. The best way to prepare for interviews and situations where critical appraisal would be indicated is to practice analysing and to practice presenting the findings. The interview is also a good opportunity for the interviewers to ask the candidates questions based on their own answers, so use this as a hook to show what you already know.

References:

(1) General Medical Council. Good Medical Practice. 2013.

(2) The UK Foundation Programme Office. The Foundation Programme Curriculum 2016. 2016.

(3) Paul M, Leibovici L, Billingham L, al. et, al. et, al. et. Systematic review or meta-analysis? Their place in the evidence hierarchy. Clin Microbiol Infect. Elsevier; 2014 Feb 1;20(2):97–100.

(4) Moher D, Liberati A, Tetzlaff J, Altman DG, Altman D. Preferred Reporting Items for Systematic Reviews and Meta-Analyses: The PRISMA Statement. PLoS Med. John Wiley & Sons; 2009 Jul 21;6(7):e1000097.

(5) Schulz KF, Altman DG, Moher D, CONSORT Group. CONSORT 2010 statement: updated guidelines for reporting parallel group randomised trials. BMJ. 2010 Mar 23; 340:c332.

(6) Von Elm E, Altman DG, Egger M, Pocock SJ, Gøtzsche PC, Vandenbroucke JP. The Strengthening the Reporting of Observational Studies in Epidemiology (STROBE) statement: guidelines for reporting observational studies.

(7) Gagnier JJ, Kienle G, Altman DG, Moher D, Sox H, Riley D, et al. The CARE Guidelines: Consensus-based Clinical Case Reporting Guideline Development. Glob Adv Heal Med. 2013 Sep 17;2(5):38–43.

(8) Huang X, Lin J, Demner-Fushman D. Evaluation of PICO as a knowledge representation for clinical questions. AMIA . Annu Symp proceedings AMIA Symp. American Medical Informatics Association; 2006;2006:359–63.

(9) Lanitis S, Karkoulias K, Sgourakis G, Brotzakis P, Armoutides V, Karaliotas C. The late effect of intraoperative wound infiltration with local anaesthetic in surgical patients; is there any? A randomized control trial. Int J Surg. 2015 Aug;20:35–40.

(10) Kimura M, Mitsui A, Kuwabara Y. Creation of the ideal gastric tube: Comparison of three methods: A prospective cohort study. Ann Med Surg. 2016 Mar;6:42–5.

Chapter 6

Ethics for the AFP

Dr Nina Cooper
Mr Ankur Khajuria

Why is ethics Important?

A good understanding of medical ethics is fundamental for progression in the integrated clinical academic training pathway. Most academic units of application (UoAs) for the AFP incorporate it as part of their 'person specification'. AFP trainees are expected to understand the general ethical principles that underpin research and should be able to describe in detail the process for ethical approval. (1) It should come as no surprise that this will come up in some way, shape or form when applying for the AFP.

There are many ways that ethics can be assessed when it comes to the AFP interview. This may require you to discuss the ethics in a research paper, or you may be given a clinical ethical scenario to evaluate.

Research ethics may require you to look at a study's methodology or the implications of its outcomes. There are plenty of examples in history of where research has gone badly wrong. Famous examples include, the Tuskegee Syphilis Study, which observed the natural history of untreated syphilis in black American men, and the Stanford Prison Experiment where participants came to harm due to the experimental conditions. (2,3) Events like these underpin why medical ethics have become a priority in all academic training curricula.

Ethics in clinical practice include issues surrounding capacity and consent, child protection, confidentiality, making a mistake, conflicts of interest, end-of-life care, religion and the national provision of healthcare. (4)

Ethical Research Principles

The Declaration of Helsinki is the main thing you need to be aware of when it comes to ethical research practices. It is 'a statement of ethical principles to provide guidance to physicians and other participants in medical research involving human subjects' and is based on the Nuremberg Code (Fig.1). (5) In summary, it states that "the well-being of the human subject should take precedence over the interests of science and society" and "ethical considerations must always take precedence over laws and regulations". (5)

When it comes to vulnerable individuals e.g. patients who are unable to give consent, surrogate consent can be given for their involvement provided that it is in the participants' best interests.

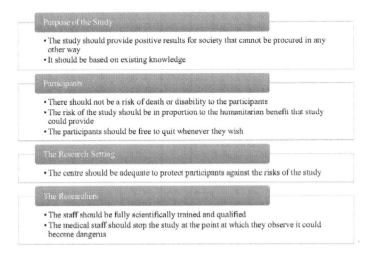

Figure 1. Key aspects of the Nuremberg code

Research Ethics Committees

Research ethics committees are made up of lay people as well as professionals, and their role is to assess applications for ethical approval by researchers. They can accept research proposals or provide feedback on how a design needs to be changed. They are important, as you can mention them in your interview when discussing how you would go about getting ethical approval for your research.

Ethical Schools of Thought

There are three key schools of thought to be aware of:

1. Utilitarianism (a consequentialist approach – i.e. the ends justify the means)
2. Paternalistic (a duty-based approach – i.e. Doctors should decide what is best as they know more)
3. Libertarian (a rights-based approach – i.e. maximizing autonomy and self-ownership)

These are useful in assessing both research papers and clinical scenarios. You can use them as a framework for dissecting a question and are handy for assimilating an argument at the interview (4,6,7).

The 4 Principles of Medical Ethics

There are four key factors that we have to consider when tackling a clinical ethical dilemma (Fig. 2): autonomy, beneficence, non-maleficence and justice. (6)

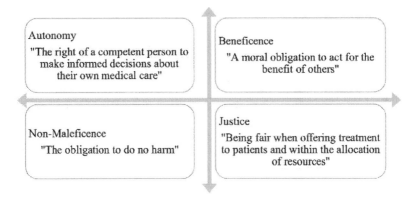

Figure 2. The four pillars of medical ethics

Ethics in the Academic Interview

Academic medicine requires that you can design ethical research, and evaluate the methodology of existing literature. You may be asked to discuss the ethics of a study at your interview, which could involve assessing the conduct of a study or the implications of the study for the population.

Classic questions you may be asked include:

- What ethical issues arise in this study?
- What ethical issues do you think the researchers had to consider?
- How would you go about gaining ethics approval?

Ethical Scenario Example:

Research

Adapted from 'The Birmingham Atrial Fibrillation Treatment of the Aged (BAFTA) Study', Mant et al. (2007) (8)

METHODS:

973 patients aged 75 years or over with atrial fibrillation were recruited from primary care and randomly assigned to warfarin (target international normalised ratio 2–3) or aspirin (75 mg per day). Follow-up was for a mean of 2.7 years (SD 1.2). The primary endpoint was fatal or disabling stroke (ischaemic or haemorrhagic), intracranial haemorrhage, or clinically significant arterial embolism. Analysis was by intention to treat.

FINDINGS:

There were 24 primary events in people assigned to warfarin and 48 primary events in people assigned to aspirin (yearly risk 1.8%vs 3.8%, relative risk 0.48, 95% CI 0.28-0.80, p=0.003; absolute yearly risk reduction 2%, 95% CI 0.7-3.2). Yearly risk of extracranial haemorrhage was 1.4% (warfarin) versus 1.6% (aspirin) (relative risk 0.87, 0.43-1.73; absolute risk reduction 0.2%, -0.7 to 1.2).

INTERPRETATION:

These data support the use of anticoagulation therapy for people aged over 75 who have atrial fibrillation, unless there are contraindications or the patient decides that the benefits are not worth the inconvenience.

Imagine you're at the interview and this is the abstract you are given. It is very likely you will be asked what you think of the ethics of this study. Here is a worked example of how you can tackle this.

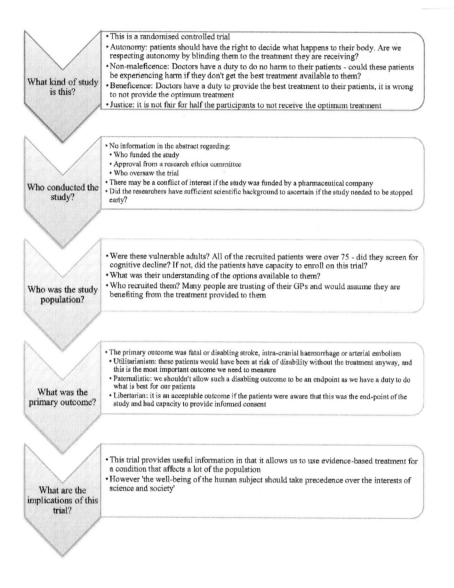

What kind of study is this?
- This is a randomised controlled trial
- Autonomy: patients should have the right to decide what happens to their body. Are we respecting autonomy by blinding them to the treatment they are receiving?
- Non-maleficence: Doctors have a duty to do no harm to their patients - could these patients be experiencing harm if they don't get the best treatment available to them?
- Beneficence: Doctors have a duty to provide the best treatment to their patients, it is wrong to not provide the optimum treatment
- Justice: it is not fair for half the participants to not receive the optimum treatment

Who conducted the study?
- No information in the abstract regarding:
  - Who funded the study
  - Approval from a research ethics committee
  - Who oversaw the trial
- There may be a conflict of interest if the study was funded by a pharmaceutical company
- Did the researchers have sufficient scientific background to ascertain if the study needed to be stopped early?

Who was the study population?
- Were these vulnerable adults? All of the recruited patients were over 75 - did they screen for cognitive decline? If not, did the patients have capacity to enroll on this trial?
- What was their understanding of the options available to them?
- Who recruited them? Many people are trusting of their GPs and would assume they are benefiting from the treatment provided to them

What was the primary outcome?
- The primary outcome was fatal or disabling stroke, intra-cranial haemorrhage or arterial embolism
  - Utilitarianism: these patients would have been at risk of disability without the treatment anyway, and this is the most important outcome we need to measure
  - Paternalistic: we shouldn't allow such a disabling outcome to be an endpoint as we have a duty to do what is best for our patients
  - Libertarian: it is an acceptable outcome if the patients were aware that this was the end-point of the study and had capacity to provide informed consent

What are the implications of this trial?
- This trial provides useful information in that it allows us to use evidence-based treatment for a condition that affects a lot of the population
- However 'the well-being of the human subject should take precedence over the interests of science and society'

Sample answer

"Having read this abstract, I have identified a few key ethical issues. Firstly, this study is a randomised control trial. Some may argue that this is the gold-standard methodology for ascertaining if one intervention is superior to another, however it poses its own ethical challenges. I immediately noticed that there were double the number of primary events in the aspirin group compared with the warfarin group. This may be considered unacceptable, as the primary event is a severely disabling or fatal outcome. One could argue that the trial should have been stopped as soon as it was noted one treatment was superior to the other.

It is the duty of a doctor to do no harm and provide beneficial treatment to their patients. It is possible that the researchers were not acting in the best interests of all participants by providing one treatment which was less effective than the other.

The study population consisted of adults over 75. I would want clarification if capacity was assessed for each participant as this group is at higher risk of cognitive decline. If these adults were vulnerable, I would be concerned that they did not provide fully-informed consent.

I also could not identify any evidence of approval for this trial from a Research Ethics Committee. There is no clear indication of the source of funding either. This makes me question if there could be a conflict of interest for the researchers."

Ethics in the Clinical Interview

Some examples are clear-cut, i.e. it is intuitive to know it is wrong to lie to your patients. However, some cases are less easy to navigate. It is useful to fall back on the four ethical principles when you get stuck in an interview scenario. The below example of an interview will allow you to see these principles put into practice.

Ethical Scenario: Clinical

Garry Jones is a 40 year old man with advanced multiple sclerosis who has been admitted to your ward. He is medically fit for discharge and you are part of the team coordinating his care. Mr Jones is bedbound and is dependent on nursing staff for all of his activities of daily living. He is able to communicate in short phrases, and can blink in response to 'yes/no' questions. He currently has carers four times a day and overnight carers too.

You discuss the potential discharge options with Mr Jones and his family. He can either return to his home with his existing package of care, or he has the option for stepdown at a nursing home where he can have 24 hour care. His wife tells you that she is struggling to cope at home with three young children, and feels responsible for her husband's care. She has clearly stated to the team and Mr Jones that she wishes for him to go to the nursing home. Mr Jones is still adamant that he wishes to return home with the existing package of care.

How do you approach this situation?

Depending on where your interview, you may have time to prepare your answer beforehand. If so, you should use the four ethics pillars above to assess the case. The sections in bold reflect the most important considerations at this case. In the interview, make sure you highlight these as you read the extract so that you address all aspects of the scenario. Often there is no right answer. Medical ethics is *primarily* about showing how you can approach a situation and knowing what your professional duties are.

This case is tricky because you are not just given information about the patient. Garry has three young children at home, and his wife has expressed she is struggling to cope. You need to remember that, although his wife's opinion is important, Garry is your patient and you must act in his best interests.

Applying The 4 Principles

Autonomy	Does the patient have capacity?
	Garry's condition has not affected his ability to understand, retain, weigh up and communicate this decision. Therefore, he has the right to decide what happens to him upon discharge
Beneficence	As Garry's doctor, you have an obligation to act in his benefit. If he is safe to be discharged home with this package of care, then his mental wellbeing will benefit from going home.
Non-Maleficence	You have an obligation to do no harm. If Garry has been assessed to be safe with a QDS package of care, you are not doing him harm by sending him home.
	Garry has young children at home – you would have to ensure that his children would not come to harm if he returns home.

| Justice | If you can provide his treatment at home, then you are allowing for an extra hospice bed to be free for another patient who cannot be managed at home. |

Sample answer

> "This situation poses a number of ethical dilemmas. I would first want to assess if Garry has capacity to make a decision. This would mean he has to be able to understand, retain and weigh up the risks and benefits of his discharge destination, and then communicate his decision to the team. Despite his limited communication, if he is still able to make informed decisions about his care, he has the right to decide on where he goes.
>
> Secondly, I would have to consider the safety of the children. If Garry's wife was unable to provide sufficient care to the children, it would become a child protection issue. However, as he is being offered day and night carers who can fulfil his care needs, I would be satisfied that his children would not come to harm.
>
> A doctor has a duty to act in the benefit of their patients, as well as to do no harm. By forcing Garry to go to a nursing home, you may actively be harming his mental health and increasing his anxiety with regard to his condition.
>
> Finally, if his needs can be met at home and it is his wish to go home, then I see no reason why this should be stopped. I would want to discuss this process with his wife and elicit her major concerns about coping with him at home. This would allow me to communicate this with his carers so that these needs can be met."

Child Protection

Child protection is also a key issue that may come up in interviews, and it is important to be aware of your duties as a doctor.

Key Points

- Child protection is everyone's responsibility; if you suspect something (Figure 3), you have a duty of care to report it.
- Child abuse encompasses emotional, physical and sexual abuse, neglect, modern slavery and trafficking.
- There will be a child protection lead at your hospital who you should contact in the event of you identifying a child who is at risk.
- If you are concerned about the welfare of a child, and the adult with them attempts to remove them from the hospital, you are within your rights to call the police. (9)

56

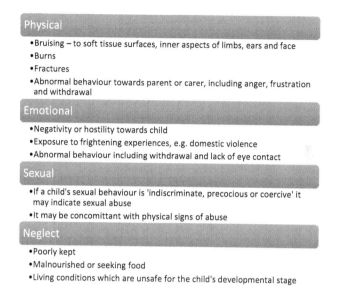

Physical
- Bruising – to soft tissue surfaces, inner aspects of limbs, ears and face
- Burns
- Fractures
- Abnormal behaviour towards parent or carer, including anger, frustration and withdrawal

Emotional
- Negativity or hostility towards child
- Exposure to frightening experiences, e.g. domestic violence
- Abnormal behaviour including withdrawal and lack of eye contact

Sexual
- If a child's sexual behaviour is 'indiscriminate, precocious or coercive' it may indicate sexual abuse
- It may be concomittant with physical signs of abuse

Neglect
- Poorly kept
- Malnourished or seeking food
- Living conditions which are unsafe for the child's developmental stage

Figure 3. Descriptors of four types of child abuse

Conclusion

An understanding of how to tackle an ethical dilemma is vital for the AFP interview, but moreover in the day-to-day life of anyone practicing medicine. (4) By having a set of tools to fall back on, you will be able to deconstruct any scenario or study that is presented to you. The most important thing to remember is that the answer to any ethical question is never as simple as 'yes' or 'no'. The interviewer will want to know that you can identify the key issues, discuss different perspectives of how these issues can be addressed (using the four principles approach, or different ethical schools of thought), and then assimilate an argument which is in line with your professional responsibilities.

In order to feel more confident in addressing these topics, you should regularly read through abstracts and identify the ethical issues that arise. You should get used to using the above steps and 'four principles' approach until it becomes second nature. Furthermore, every day clinicians are confronted with ethical dilemmas. On any ward there will be someone who is having decisions made in their best interests, whether it is due to a temporary lack of capacity, such as in delirium, or a more chronic process. Attending the wards regularly will help you to identify how doctors go about tackling these issues in 'real life', and will ultimately make your arguments at interview genuine and informed.

References:

(1) The Foundation Programme. (2017). The Foundation Programme - Academic. [online] Available at: http://www.foundationprogramme.nhs.uk/pages/fp-afp/faqs/academic [Accessed 24 Aug. 2017].

(2) Zimbardo PG. On the ethics of intervention in human psychological research: With special reference to the Stanford prison experiment. Cognition. 1973;2:243-256.

(3) Brandt AM. Racism and research: the case of the Tuskegee Syphilis Study. Hastings Cent Rep. 1978;8:21-29.

(4) Iyalomhe GBS. Medical ethics and ethical dilemmas. Niger J Med. 2009;18:8-16.

(5) General Assembly of the World Medical Association. World Medical Association Declaration of Helsinki: ethical principles for medical research involving human subjects. J Am Coll Dent 2014;81:14.

(6) Beauchamp TL, Childress JF. Principles of biomedical ethics. : Oxford University Press, USA; 2001.pp 57-377

(7) Gillon R. Medical ethics: four principles plus attention to scope. BMJ. 1994;309:184.

(8) Mant J, Hobbs FR, Fletcher K, Roalfe A, Fitzmaurice D, Lip GY, et al. Warfarin versus aspirin for stroke prevention in an elderly community population with atrial fibrillation (the Birmingham Atrial Fibrillation Treatment of the Aged Study, BAFTA): a randomised controlled trial. The Lancet. 2007;370: 493-503.

(9) National Institute for Clinical and Health Excellence. Child maltreatment: when to suspect maltreatment in under 18s. Available at: https://www.nice.org.uk/guidance/cg89. [Accessed 22 Aug. 2017]

Chapter 7

Curriculum Vitae and Portfolios

Mr Ankur Khajuria

The ideal scenario would be to have an immaculate portfolio and CV, with evidence of you achievements, ready prior to applying for the AFP. Not only do some deaneries request a CV as part of the application process, but a well organised CV/portfolio also makes it very easy to identify key achievements to package into your white space answers. However, most candidates will not have thought about portfolios and CVs prior to AFP applications. In this chapter, you will receive guidance on how to organise a CV and a portfolio. This will be useful not just for AFP but also for future applications (core training/ACF) where a portfolio is a mandatory part of the application.

Why bother?

At a time when competition for posts (higher clinical training/academic training/consultant jobs) is fierce, having maintained a high quality, accurate CV and portfolio will help facilitate your career progression. (1) Remember, for the AFP only 5% of UK medical students will secure a post. (2) Both CV and portfolios are a record of achievement and should showcase why you are a suitable candidate for a role. A CV is a pre-requisite for some AFP programmes and there are dedicated portfolio interview stations for core/higher training. Indeed, it is also an easily accessible source of past experiences, achievements and examples of various personal attributes, crucial for completing application forms and preparing for interview. It can be difficult to recall past achievements if there is no record and if one needs to produce a CV on short notice, if you have not been maintaining one, it will be a big nuisance trying to put one together.

Having maintained a CV since Year 3 of medical school has allowed me to approach academic supervisors with confidence and has been an indispensable source of evidence to back up my skills and qualities. In fact, it is almost considered unprofessional to approach a senior lecturer/professor for a research project without attaching a CV. It also greatly facilitated my AFP application when I could easily pick out my best achievements to highlight in the form.

Likewise, portfolios are a fantastic way to keep a record of achievements. Indeed for AFP and future applications, it is a crucial source (for example, for core surgical training, the portfolio is worth 33% of the marks).

How to organise the CV and portfolio

To understand this, it is important to think about the CanMEDS clover. (3) This describes 6 domains that make the "medical expert." One way to start organising your past achievements, is to divide them according to the CanMEDS clover. This will allow you to make a list of achievements and then start to collect the evidence for those achievements. Believe me, this takes much longer than you think, so start as soon as possible! Evidence is absolutely key, so if you attended a course and are missing a certificate, email the course organiser. Chase medical students for feedback forms for your teaching.

CV components

Personal details

Here you should include your date of birth; address; email address; telephone; marital Status; nationality; memberships and membership numbers (e.g Medical Defence Union; British Medical Association)

Education

Here, include school (and grades), university and post-graduation.
In university section, include the degrees you have received. If you have impressive content, you may wish to have subheadings.

For example, for medical school, you may have a section for your course performance:
MBBS (or equivalent):
-Distinction in Surgery (Top 5%)
-XXX prize for best performance [include names of prizes and include percentages and ranks if impressive]

BSc (Hons), 1st class honours in XXX
-XXX Prize for best overall performance
-Any research grants

A separate section can be: "University - academic honors, prizes and research"
This can include other prizes/awards which do not fit in the medical school course bracket (ie external awards, e.g RCS, RSM).

Publications

Include all your publications (first author and high impact publications at the top). You can divide as: 1) Full-text 2) Abstracts

Include full details (including your name in bold), for example:
Khajuria A, Maruthappu M, Nagendran M, Shalhoub J, What about the surgeon? International Journal of Surgery. 2013;11:18-21 [PMID: 23246870].
Presentations

Divide into oral and poster presentations. Once again, include the presentations you yourself presented, at the top. Include full details as below (highlight your name in bold):

The Reporting Quality of Randomised Controlled Trials in Ophthalmological Surgery in 2011 –a systematic review. 117th Annual Meeting of the Japanese Ophthalmological Society 2013, Tokyo, Japan, 4 April 2014. **Khajuria A** [presenter], Yao AC, Camm CF, Edison E, Agha R.

Audits

List the title of the audit, the name of the people who carried out the audit; the standard used; any intervention; the outcome/change implementation; include your own role at the bottom: "conception, design, data collection, analysis, presentation" etc.

Courses and conferences
Include any relevant courses and conferences that demonstrate your interest.

Teaching

Things to include: teaching qualifications; if you have designed and delivered a teaching programme; anatomy demonstrator etc

Leadership/Management/Teamwork

Head/Secretary/Academic officer of Student Union, Sports captain, Choir conductor Head of medical school conference

Include more impressive stuff at the top

Other hobbies and interests

Recruiters are looking for balanced individuals and mentioning any sports/music etc you are involved is advised. Also include any volunteering experience. However, remember that unless you did rowing for Great Britain (or an activity of that standard!), this section will not compensate for lack of content in the other sections of the CV, e.g. publications, prizes

Referees

Include any referees, their title and place of work and a working email.

A similar format can be followed for portfolios. Ensure content pages are present at the start of any new section. An A4 ring binder with file pockets is recommended. Needless to say the portfolio needs to be professional and aesthetically appealing.

The above recommendation has worked for others and me. However, it is important to note that there is no set way of arranging your CV and portfolio. If the content is presented well and you know exactly where to find a piece of evidence (quickly and under pressure in an interview setting, for example), then that is also an acceptable format to use.

In summary, if you are reading this weeks/months before your AFP application (or indeed before core or higher training), it is important to start collecting the evidence now for your portfolio and arranging your CV. Having invested time early will help you immensely when job applications come round. Good luck!

References:

(1) Medford AR. How to improve your curriculum vitae. Br J Hosp Med (Lond). 2013;74: C98-101.

2) The Foundation Programme. (2017). The Foundation Programme - Academic. [online] Available at: http://www.foundationprogramme.nhs.uk/pages/fp-afp/faqs/academic [Accessed 17 Aug. 2017].

(3) Ologunde R, Di salvo I, Khajuria A. The canmeds scholar: the neglected competency in tomorrow's doctors. *Adv Med Educ Pract* 2014; 5: 383–4.

Chapter 8

Practice questions on critical appraisal and clinical scenarios

Mr Ankur Khajuria

Below are included some research abstracts and clinical scenarios for you to practice in a group. In fact, you should be refining your critical appraisal abilities by regularly appraising articles in peer-reviewed journals. In terms of clinical scenarios, practice saying your primary survey (as per chapter 4) and ask registrars and consultants on your clinical rotations to quiz you on common scenarios.

Abstract 1

Please access the abstract for the following paper (1):

Sorafenib in advanced hepatocellular carcinoma. Llovet JM et al. NEJM. 2008 [PMID: 18650514]

Questions/Discussion points:

Study design – What is a phase 3 study and how does it differ from phase 0,1 and 2 studies?

- Phase 0: first in human (e.g. pharmacodynamics)
- Phase 1: side effects (safety)
- Phase 2: side effects & efficacy in larger population (efficacy against placebo)
- Phase 3: side effects & efficacy in even larger population (confirm efficacy)

Why randomise? How can you randomise?

  o Reduce bias
  o Centralised, computerised randomisation

- What is a second planned interim analysis?

- Pre-agreed time-point during study for analysis – can stop trial early

Statistics:

- Why use median overall survival rather than mean?
  - Resistant to outliers
  - Doesn't require complete data (i.e. finite survival) – will be unchanged once data collected up until certain number (c.f. mean requires all deaths)
- Define hazard ratio
  - Survival analysis; ratio of hazard rates
  - Calculated by Kaplan-Meier survival curves
  - Assumed to be constant over time – applies to any given time-point
- Define a P value
- Define a confidence interval
- Define intention-to-treat analysis
- Stratification of patients before randomisation was carried out – why?

Ethics:

- Can you discuss some of the ethics relevant to this study
  - Study stopped early
  - Ethical procedures in setting up an RCT
  - Placebo
    - Informed consent
    - Ethics committee
    - Declaration of Helsinki – ethical principles for human experimentation, including informed decisions, patient autonomy.
  - Who decides on stopping an RCT early?

Clinical translation:

- Clinical considerations: side effects, cost-benefit for extra survival
- Can you think of how frequent side effects might introduce bias into the study?

o Compromise blinding

Abstract 2

Please access the abstract for the following paper (2):

Rivaroxaban versus warfarin in nonvalvular atrial fibrillation. Patel MR et al, NEJM. 2011;365: 883-891.

Study design:
- Define double-blinding – why is it done?
- This study has a double-dummy design – what is that?
  o Patients in both arms take placebo tablets (so both arms end up taking same tablets) to maintain blinding
- How did the study randomise participants?
  o Central 24-hour computerized, automated voice-response system to randomise

Statistics:
- What is a hazard ratio:
  o Survival analysis; ratio of hazard rates
  o Calculated by Kaplan-Meier survival curves
  o Assumed to be constant over time – applies to any given time-point
  o E.g. treated patient on Rivaroxaban who has not had a stroke/emboli by certain time, has 0.79 chance of having a stroke/emobli by a certain time as compared to a control group participant
- Define a P value
- Define a confidence interval?
- What does non-inferiority mean? Why do studies test for it?
  o Showing that rivaroxaban is as good as warfarin – but offering other benefits, e.g. safety & patient acceptability
- What is a per-protocol analysis?

- o Data considered from only those patients who received the treatment and complied with protocol through to completion
  - o Non-inferiority is also best tested in patients actually taking the treatment (rather than including those who dropped out in intention-to-treat)
- What is intention-to-treat and why is it important?

Ethics:
- What ethical considerations are relevant in this study?
  - o Active control (i.e. warfarin) rather than placebo
  - o Ethical procedures in setting up an RCT:
    - Informed consent
    - Ethics committee
    - Declaration of Helsinki – ethical principles for human experimentation, including informed decisions, patient autonomy.

Clinical translation:
- Cost-benefit consideration

CLINICAL SCENARIOS

You are the house officer on call. Two bleeps come in, one after the other:

A 55-year old man in the oncology clinic who is here for his weekly chemotherapy. He has no history of any other health condition but has had some abdominal pain for the past couple of hours and wants some painkillers. He's keen to go home as soon as possible to see his son's football match.

If candidate asks for observations - increased respiratory rate, feeling a bit short of breath

SOCRATES - pain is epigastric, but also made worse by breathing in. Nausea, but he isn't sure if this is the chemo.

Differential diagnosis:

- MI
- PE (cancer)
- surgical acute abdomen - esp pancreatitis/ulcer
- medical causes of abdominal pain including infection/sepsis, acidosis

An 87 year old lady on the general medical ward has fallen out of bed.

Candidate should consider:
If she has sustained an injury (particularly head - subdural and hip fracture)
Why has she fallen?
Causes: ?Cardiac ?Respiratory ?Neurological

You are the house officer on call. Two bleeps come in, one after the other:

47 year old lady on the oncology ward who has been having chemotherapy for her colorectal cancer. She's been vomiting all day and hasn't been able to keep any food or fluids down. She has a K^+ of 2.7mmol/L on a VBG

Hypokalaemia of 2.7 on blood gas

Risks? – arrhythmia
Management of hypokalemia:
ECG
Oral supplementation insufficient here, IV required
How fast can you give K, what is the risk of giving K too fast?

Observations from a 75 year old man who is three days post-op after a right hemicolectomy for caecal volvulus.

HR 86

BP 145/84

RR 26

T 35.8

SpO2 97% on room air

Sepsis

Sepsis 6

Questions:

What do you say to each nurse on the phone?

How would you prioritize?

-This should include a rationale, which is in essence a differential diagnosis

-Initial investigations and management plan

REFERENCES:

(1) Llovet JM, Ricci S, Mazzaferro V, Hilgard P, Gane E, Blanc JF, et al. Sorafenib in advanced hepatocellular carcinoma. NEJM, 2008;359(4): 378-390.

(2) Patel MR, Mahaffey KW, Garg J, Pan G, Singer DE, Hacke W, et al. Rivaroxaban versus warfarin in nonvalvular atrial fibrillation. NEJM. 2011;365: 883-891.

Printed in Great Britain
by Amazon